A B C D E F G

N O P Q R S T

Meet big **R** and little **r.**

Trace each letter with your finger and say its name.

R is for

robot

R is also for

Rr Story

This little **r**ed **r**obot
is **r**eally awesome!

This **r**obot can **r**ide a **r**am.

She can **r**ace a **r**abbit.

She can **r**un under a **r**ainbow...

and smell all the **r**oses.

This **r**obot can play **r**ock and **r**oll with a **r**eally awesome **r**ooster.

Root, toot!
Rock-a-doodle-do!